BEETHOVEN

Sonata quasi una fantasia

in C sharp minor

Op. 27 No. 2 ('Moonlight')

Edited by BARRY COOPER

Fingering by DAVID WARD

The Associated Board of the Royal Schools of Music

First published in 2007 as part of *The 35 Piano Sonatas* by
The Associated Board of the Royal Schools of Music (Publishing) Limited,
24 Portland Place, London W1B 1LU, United Kingdom.

AB 2802d

Music setting: Andrew Jones
Text setting: Hope Services (Abingdon) Ltd, England

Cover by Vermillion Design, incorporating Beethoven's signature from a letter to
Franz Brentano, 12 November 1821 (Beethoven-Haus, Bonn).

THE 35 PIANO SONATAS
Edited by Barry Cooper

This sonata is taken from the complete three-volume edition of Beethoven's 35 piano sonatas published by the Associated Board (2007). The edition aims firstly to present the musical text of each sonata precisely as Beethoven intended it (as far as this is possible), through a detailed reassessment of all the relevant sources, while indicating places where there is room for doubt; and secondly to give sufficient explanation of the meaning of his notation, since notation has evolved considerably since his time and certain unwritten assumptions of the period have to be spelt out today. Each sonata is provided with detailed editorial notes offering informed guidance about many of the more problematical passages, where either the text or its interpretation is in some way ambiguous. For further information about problems associated with the sources and the interpretation of the music, see the general Introduction printed at the beginning of each of the three volumes in the complete edition. The editorial method for the complete edition is given below.

EDITORIAL METHOD

A single source of each sonata, normally the autograph score or first edition, has been used as the copy-text, and all deviations from it have been indicated, either on the page itself or in the Commentary to the individual sonata. However, it often happens that no source consistently reflects Beethoven's intentions better than any other: a manuscript copy or the first printed edition may incorporate corrections and late revisions that are not in his autograph score, yet it might also include copying errors. Thus wherever the copy-text is believed to be inferior to another source, the readings from that source have been adopted as the main text. The aim has been to reproduce as closely as possible what are believed to be Beethoven's final intentions for the written text, even though these may not all be found in one source and are occasionally ambiguous. In parallel passages (such as an exposition and recapitulation) random minor discrepancies sometimes occur, e.g. in slurring, note lengths or occasionally an actual inconspicuous note. Beethoven seems not to have been bothered by such minutiae, and therefore nor should we: they have been allowed to stand as slight irregularities. Where one of the two versions seems positively faulty, however, it has been brought into line with the other, and the change noted. Distinguishing between minor variants and positive errors is a matter of editorial judgement and not always clear cut.

The edition matches the copy-text exactly apart from the following points:

a) Titles have been standardized, with the original titles noted in the Commentary. Certain performance instructions have also been standardized, e.g. *cres* as *cresc.*, *dol* as *dolce* and *ligato* as *legato*, as have turns printed upside down or with a qualifying accidental above instead of below the sign. Bar numbers have been added.

b) Redundant accidentals have normally been retained except on tied notes or notes repeated almost immediately. They can be useful as cautionary accidentals. Cautionary accidentals from secondary sources have also been incorporated in places. Any extra ones needed are shown in small type.

c) Editorial suggestions for certain ornaments are placed above the stave, and the old arpeggiando sign is modernized.

d) Minor notational changes have sometimes been made, provided the change could not affect the interpretation. For example, the clef, the direction of note stems (where it has no significance) and the distribution of notes between staves are occasionally altered for greater clarity. In general, however, the copy-text has been followed, even if the notation is slightly unconventional, since it could help explain the role and function of the notes. This principle applies also to the presence or absence of internal double bars, which have not been silently modernized.

e) Original beaming of quavers and semiquavers has been retained from the copy-text (except in the very rare places where it is positively misleading), but variants in beaming in other sources have not been noted. In some places the original beaming provides clues about articulation and phrasing, although elsewhere it may have no significance.

f) Beethoven's own fingerings appear in large type, similar in size to what was common in his day. They are supplemented by recommended editorial fingering by David Ward (in normal type), and by occasional suggestions for which hand to use, indicated by $\lceil$ (for left hand) or $\lfloor$ (for right). But performers should work out for themselves what fingering best suits their own unique hands, and editorial fingering has been kept somewhat restricted so as not to clutter the page.

g) Editorial ties and slurs, which are added only where their omission is believed to be an oversight, are marked thus: ⌢ Editorial extensions of existing ties and slurs are shown by broken lines. Where slurs are only fractionally short (i.e. by less than one note), however, they have been extended without indication. Slurs that are slightly too long have likewise been curtailed.

h) Other editorial additions, whether corrections or supplementary performance recommendations, are shown by means of small type or square brackets, and are generally kept to a minimum (restricted mainly to amplification based on directly parallel passages, clarifying uncertainties, and correcting apparently erroneous signs).

i) The distinction between staccato dots and dashes has been retained only where it appears significant or the autograph is unambiguous. Elsewhere dots, and symbols between dot and dash, have been replaced by dashes, except under slurs, where dots are retained and any dashes found in printed sources are replaced by dots.

j) Where dynamics are slightly misaligned in early editions, as often happens, they have been adjusted using common sense. Where the misalignment is more substantial or uncertain, the amendment has been noted. Where Beethoven's autograph survives, the alignment of dynamics is carefully followed.

k) All other deviations from the copy-text are listed in the Commentary. Superior readings from secondary sources are incorporated and the fact noted. Other major variants in secondary sources are also indicated, but minor variants in secondary sources, including obvious misreadings and omissions, are generally not listed unless they are considered possibly significant.

Summary of Editorial Additions:

Bar numbers

Crossed ties and slurs

Broken-line extensions to slurs

Small notes (other than grace notes), accidentals and other symbols

Everything within [ ]

All fingering except that shown in large type

⌈ or ⌊ indicating which hand to use

Supplementary staves recommending interpretation of ornament signs

The Commentary for each sonata, besides discussing textual and notational problems in the sources, also includes suggestions on matters of performance. A few of these (marked DFT and CCz repectively) are derived from Donald Tovey's notes in the Associated Board's old edition (London, 1931) or from Czerny 1970 (see References). The metronome marks in movement headings are Carl Czerny's. Where applicable, these indicate his fastest and slowest recommended speeds (see general Introduction).

In the Commentary, abbreviations for notes are used as, for example: **31.rh.6** denotes the sixth symbol (note, grace note or rest) in the right-hand (i.e. upper) stave in bar 31. Alternatively, in place of **rh/lh**, individual voices may be specified, namely **s** (soprano), **a** (alto), **t** (tenor), **b** (bass), **s2** (2nd soprano); hence **31.a.6** denotes the sixth alto symbol.

First- or second-time bars are shown in the form **31*a*** or **31*b*****. Thus **31*a*.a2.6** denotes the sixth symbol in the second-alto part in bar 31 (first time).

Pitches are given as *CC–BB, C–B, c–b, c¹–b¹, c²–b², c³–b³, c⁴–b⁴*; *c¹* is middle C.

Bibliographical references and further reading

Barth, George, *The Pianist as Orator: Beethoven and the Transformation of Keyboard Style*, Ithaca and London, 1992.

Brandenburg, Sieghard, ed., *Ludwig van Beethoven: Briefwechsel Gesamtausgabe*, 7 vols., Munich, 1996–8.

Clementi, Muzio, *Introduction to the Art of Playing on the Piano Forte*, London, 1801 (reprinted New York, 1974).

Cooper, Barry, 'Beethoven's Appoggiaturas: Long or Short?', *Early Music*, xxxi (2003), 165–78.

Czerny, Carl, *On the Proper Performance of All Beethoven's Works for the Piano*, ed. Paul Badura-Skoda, Vienna, 1970.

Jeffery, Brian, ed., *Ludwig van Beethoven: The 32 Piano Sonatas in reprints of the first and early editions*, London, 1989.

Newman, William S., *Beethoven on Beethoven: Playing His Piano Music His Way*, New York and London, 1988.

Rosenblum, Sandra P., *Performance Practices in Classic Piano Music*, Bloomington and Indianapolis, 1988.

BARRY COOPER
Manchester, 2008

SONATA QUASI UNA FANTASIA
in C sharp minor, Op. 27 No. 2 ('Moonlight')

HISTORY

The famous 'Moonlight' Sonata derives its nickname ultimately from Ludwig Rellstab's novel *Theodor* (published 1824), where a character suggests that the first movement of the sonata portrays moonlight over a lake. The name was popularized in the 1850s by Wilhelm von Lenz, although his account of the Rellstab source is inaccurate (see Michael Ladenburger and Friederike Grigat, *Beethovens "Mondschein-Sonate"*, Bonn, 2003, pp. 22–3). Czerny also refers to the movement as 'a night scene'. Yet there is no evidence that the movement had any specific nocturnal associations in Beethoven's mind, and it is significant that the comments of Rellstab and Czerny were not made until after John Field had composed some 'nocturnes' in which this style of broken-chord accompaniment and lyrical melody was widely exploited. (The style later reappeared in Chopin's nocturnes.) Beethoven's own title is far more revealing: 'Sonata quasi una fantasia' – Sonata in the manner of a fantasy or fantasia. Like its companion Op. 27 No. 1, the sonata has an unusually free formal structure, with a greater sense of continuity between movements than was normal in a sonata. Another fantasia-like feature is the relative brevity (at least on paper) of the first two movements, which results in a very end-orientated structure, with the main weight of the sonata falling on the finale.

Sketches for the work are found almost exclusively in the Sauer Sketchbook, which was purchased from Beethoven's estate by Ignaz Sauer and then systematically dismembered by him. Many pages are now missing, including some that presumably contained sketches for the first two movements, but five leaves are known containing sketches for the finale. They date from summer 1801, around the time that Beethoven wrote two long letters to friends telling them for the first time about his increasingly poor hearing. It would be wrong, however, to assume that this sonata is in some way an expression of his personal despair at that time, for, as indicated above, it has no explicit programmatic associations. By November that year Beethoven was feeling decidedly more cheerful, a situation brought about, as he reported, by 'a dear charming girl who loves me and whom I love' (Brandenburg ed., *Briefwechsel*, No. 70). The girl was evidently Countess Giulietta Guicciardi (1784–1856), who received some piano lessons from Beethoven about that time and became the dedicatee of this sonata. The sonata was not composed specially for her, however: according to her own account, Beethoven originally planned to dedicate a different work to her (the Rondo in G, Op. 51 No. 2), but withdrew it from her when he needed something urgently for Countess Lichnowsky, and gave Giulietta the dedication of the 'Moonlight' Sonata instead. In 1803 Giulietta married Count Wenzel Gallenberg and the couple moved away to Italy.

Like the two previous sonatas, this one was published by Giovanni Cappi, who announced the publication of all three on 3 March 1802. It quickly became popular, and the first movement is one of the most celebrated in all Beethoven's works.

COMMENTARY

The sources used are as follows:

A (copy-text): Autograph score, Bonn, Beethoven-Archiv, BH 60. 16 surviving folios. (See facsimile edition, Vienna, 1921; new facsimile edition, Bonn, 2004). The first and last folios of the original MS are lost; they contained the title page, bars 1–13 of the first movement and the last three bars of the finale.

B (first edition): *Sonata quasi una fantasia per il clavicembalo o piano-forte composta e dedicata alla Damigella Contessa Giulietta Guicciardi da Luigi van Beethoven Opera 27. No. 2. In Vienna presso Gio. Cappi…*, pp. 2–15. Exemplar in Vienna, Nationalbibliothek, Hoboken Collection, S.H. Beethoven 134 (see facsimile in Jeffery 1989).

C (another exemplar of the first edition): London, British Library, e.345.l. A later impression than **B**, with slightly different address for Cappi, but the musical text is identical.

The present edition is based mainly on **A**. The first edition was engraved from either **A** or a lost copy, but Beethoven appears to have checked the edition and made minor corrections. Other corrections may have been made by the editor or engraver. Variants in **B/C** include minor errors not listed below, occasional extra cautionary accidentals (some of which have been adopted here), and a few corrections, which have been incorporated here but are listed below. More complex variants are discussed in the commentaries on each movement. Corrections adopted from **B/C** are:

1st movement. Bar 21.t.3: **A** omits ♮; 53–4.rh: slur stops after 53 in **A** (at change of line).

2nd movement. 19.s.1: **A** omits ♭; 32.rh.1: **A** omits staccato; 33.b.2: **A** omits ♮; 41–2.t, 49–50.t, 50–1.t, 55–6.t, 57–8.t: **A** omits ties; 60.lh.2: **A** omits rest.

3rd movement. 7, 16, 18: **A** omits staccatos on rh.13 14 (and on 15.lh.1–8); 18.lh.7: **A** omits ♯; 23–4.rh.4–6: **A** omits slurs; 55.lh.5: **A** omits clef; 65a.lh.5–8, 65b.lh.1–8: **A** omits staccatos; 78.rh.2, 78.lh.3, 79.lh.2, 80.rh.2, 80.lh.5, 81.lh.5: **A** omits ♮ signs; 95.rh.1: **A** omits ♯; 97.rh.1–2: **A** has redundant slur (there is another in all sources in 153.rh.1–2); 110.b.2: **A** has dotted quaver (plus tie); 114.lh.5–8: **A** omits staccatos (both voices); 115.t.1: **A** omits ♯; 128.rh: **A** omits lower ♮ and places **p** one note late; 129.rh.1, 134.rh.12, 134.lh.2: **A** omits ♮ signs; 136.rh.2: **A** omits lower ♯; 160, 162: **A** omits staccatos on rh.13–14; 169.lh.1–2: **A** omits slur; 172.a.2: **A** omits ♯; 172–3.a.2–3: **A** omits ties; 173: **A** omits dynamics; 174.rh.1–2: **A** omits slur; 177–8.lh: **A** omits middle tie.

Adagio sostenuto (♩ = 54–63)

This Adagio's supposed connection with moonlight and night-time is purely speculative, as explained above, although it is not wholly inappropriate in view of the serenade-like figuration. Czerny's suggestion that it portrays a scene 'in which the voice of a complaining spirit is heard at a distance' is also pertinent, for there is no doubt that the movement has a strongly lamenting character; moreover, according to Edwin Fischer (*Beethoven's Pianoforte Sonatas*, London, 1959, p.63) Beethoven once wrote out a strikingly similar passage from immediately after the death of the Commendatore in Mozart's *Don Giovanni*, significantly transposing it to C sharp minor. As for Czerny's idea of distance, this matches Beethoven's instruction to play the movement very softly almost throughout, and with pedal that might suggest a muffled echo from afar. Czerny adds that the movement is 'highly poetical, and therefore perfectly comprehensible to any one.'

The correct speed of the movement is difficult to judge. Recordings range widely, from a total time of under four minutes to over eight (see Sandra Mangsen, 'Tempo in the first movement of the "Moonlight" Sonata Op. 27 No. 2: Some evidence from early recordings', *Arietta*, iii (2002), 17–28). The present editor's preference is for a total time of a little over five minutes. The heading 'Adagio' suggests a very slow tempo, but the time signature indicates two beats per bar, not four. This combination of adagio and 2/2 metre is uncommon in Beethoven, and the only example with an authentic metronome mark appears to be in his Fourth Symphony, where the crotchet is 66, but even this is not directly comparable since the figuration is less dense than here. Czerny's suggestions of 54 to 63 for the present movement, resembling a 'moderate Andante', seem acceptable, but there should surely be much flexibility of tempo during such a movement, especially around the ends of phrases. A slightly slower tempo is also possible, but it is essential to ensure that the music moves sufficiently fast to preserve the *alla breve* pulse, with the main beats slightly more accented than the off-beat crotchets. When the melody enters (bar 5) it should introduce a new tone colour and be considerably louder than the triplets, which need to be kept extremely quiet wherever they accompany the melody. Emphasizing the melody in this manner also helps to keep the music moving, despite the slow tempo.

The initial instruction states, 'This whole movement must be played very delicately and with pedal,' and the instruction 'senza sordino' (without dampers, i.e. with pedal) is repeated between the staves. There has been much debate about whether Beethoven wanted the pedal held continuously or merely used throughout with appropriate changes, as suggested by Czerny. On a modern instrument there is an enormous difference between these two effects, but on an instrument of 1800 the difference was far less, since the sound sustained a much shorter time, creating much less blurring. If you have a chance to play such an instrument, or hear a recording of one, listen particularly to the effect of the sustaining pedal – preferably using this movement. The effect can, however, be mimicked fairly closely on a modern instrument by carefully controlled half-pedalling. If this is attempted, it is essential to listen very carefully and judge the sound finely, holding the pedal down as much as you can manage without creating an unpleasantly discordant blurring. The soft pedal may also be used in this movement: Czerny reports that Beethoven customarily employed it throughout except in bars 32–9. Whether or not the soft pedal is used, it is all too easy to forget after a few bars that most of this movement should be played either *p* or *pp*.

5.s.4, 6.s.3 etc. Play the semiquaver immediately after the last triplet note. Although some composers of the period used dotted notation as a substitute for triplet crotchet plus quaver, Beethoven seems always to have intended the two rhythms to be differentiated when he used this combination. Czerny, who evidently studied this sonata with Beethoven, insists that the semiquaver should follow the triplet. Equally significant, when the movement was originally engraved, many of the semiquavers were placed directly above the last triplet note, but the plates were then altered (at some expense and inconvenience) to show the semiquavers further to the right. It may also be relevant that, when Beethoven wrote the 'Appassionata' Sonata (Op. 57) a few years later, he combined dotted figures with triplets in his sketches, but in the autograph he showed his intentions more clearly by replacing the dotted figures with tied crotchet and semiquaver, to ensure that the final note in each group was played after the triplet. On the rare occasions when he wanted a 2+1 rhythm against accompanying triplets he wrote it as such, e.g. in his Fantasia Op. 77, bar 2.

16.s.1 'The C natural with particular expression' (CCz). It can be held back slightly, with extra emphasis, and might also be played slightly after the alto, even if your hand is big enough for this not to be necessary.

20.lh.1 Lower note is *DD♯* in all sources, a note that is harmonically absurd and was not even available on Beethoven's piano. It illustrates well the danger of placing too much faith in a composer's autograph score.

27–37 This passage was written out twice in the autograph, with version **A1** superseded by **A2**. In **A1** bar 27 is marked *p*, but this is missing in **A2**, which has no dynamic mark in bar 27 or the beginning of bar 28. Beethoven evidently sensed the omission when checking proofs for the first edition, but decided to place *p* in bar 28 instead, preceded by *decresc.*, as appears in **B/C** but not **A1** or **A2**.

32–35 'remarkably crescendo and accelerando up to forte, which in bars 36 to 39 again decreases' (CCz). There is no sign of this long crescendo and diminuendo in any of the sources, however, and so you should not feel obliged to follow Czerny's recommendation. Tovey's view is entirely different: 'not...a crescendo at all, but...a cumulative effect of long abstention from anything of the sort'.

52, 54 In **B/C** the crescendos peak earlier, roughly matching bars 16 and 18. But what Beethoven wrote implies that the precise location of the peak is relatively unimportant, provided the swelling is expressive.

62–5 The crescendos and diminuendos probably apply to both hands both times, despite their actual position, which seems to relate to the amount of space available in **A**.

69 The instruction *Attacca...* implies that there should be no pause or silence between this movement and the start of the next. The change of mood and register should be completely sudden.

Allegretto (♩. = 76–84)

A complete contrast of mood from the first movement, this short Allegretto in minuet-and-trio form needs to be played with lightness and delicacy, and 'agreeably, [rather] than with gaiety' (CCz). Czerny's suggested speed seems about right, and the music should skip along without sounding hurried. Observe the staccatos carefully, especially those at the ends of slurs such as in bars 2 and 6, which can float off without any accent. Most of Beethoven's staccato dashes are wrongly replaced by dots in **B/C**, but there would scarcely be any difference in practice at this speed. As in the first movement, care must be taken that the dynamic level remains quiet almost throughout. This applies even in the heavier Trio section, where only isolated notes are marked louder. In **A** Beethoven actually cancelled a crescendo in bar 49, and another one in bar 53, leaving only a very short one in bar 57.

19.a.2 Source **A** has *d¹* (preceded by a redundant ♭); but this gives incorrect harmony and part-writing, and was corrected to *e¹* in **B/C**. Perhaps Beethoven intended *e¹*♭♭ at one stage.

36 In **A** the Trio begins on a new page, with a blank system at the bottom of the previous one. This suggests perhaps a slight gap in performance before the Trio, especially since the time signature is repeated as if it were a separate movement. (The initial start-of-repeat sign is also absent in the sources.)

36–42.rh Observe the slightly irregular disposition of the *sf* marks, which are avoided altogether in the second half of the Trio.

37.lh etc. In **A** the *fp* is always placed beside the tied tenor note, but in **B/C** it is placed more approximately, as if applying to the bass as well. If the bass note is louder than *p* in these bars it will hardly matter, but it must be *p* in the following bars each time. Notice that the bass is not marked legato, and can be detached.

51.rh Slur is in **B/C** only, and may be merely an editorial change to match l.h.

Presto (♩ = 80–92)

'The whole extremely impetuous, and with a powerful, clear, and brilliant touch' (CCz). The sorrowful broken chords and repeated G♯s of the opening of the first movement re-emerge here transformed into a stormy, agitated finale, which remains in minor keys almost throughout. Even the apparent majors prove to be mere prolongations of either a dominant (bars 65–6) or a Neapolitan (bars 78–81) of an ensuing minor key, making this one of the darkest movements in Beethoven's entire output. Like the first two movements, its emotion is very concentrated and varies little in character, as is implied by Czerny's comment above. But it is in full-scale sonata form, and there is some contrast between the driving, agitated first subject and the more lyrical second subject (bars 21ff.). For most pianists, the direction *presto* will simply be an invitation to play the movement as fast as they can, though Czerny's suggested speed can be taken as a target or rough guide.

1–8 'The quavers in the bass, very staccato' (CCz). The word *agitato* is shown here roughly as in **A**; in **B/C** it was incorporated into the movement heading as 'Presto Agitato.' As in so many Beethoven movements, there is a great danger in this one of playing too loud too often. Notice that there is no crescendo here until bar 7 (though Czerny puts one in bar 2), and a single loud chord in bar 2 (though Czerny marks both chords *ff*). The first sustained *forte* in the entire sonata does not begin until bar 9. The sources clearly show that the pedal, which Beethoven notated with 'senza sordino' as in the first movement, is to continue through the two chords on each occasion, and be lifted ('con sordino') at the start of the next bar.

6–8 The *sf* marks continue to apply to both hands, though only written once each bar.

10.t, 12.t The slurs may be intended to continue across the bar-line to bars 11 and 13; but they clearly do not do so in the recapitulation (bars 111 and 113).

21 'The sudden *piano* must have time to speak' (DFT). A hint of rubato here can help, but Tovey usefully recommends making the *piano* chiefly in the l.h. The first r.h. note may be lost if it is too quiet.

22.rh.1–3 Beethoven's use of only two beams for the ornament implies that he expected triplet semiquavers (beginning, as usual, on the beat), leaving only a quaver for the main note. Aim to play the ornament quicker if you wish; but if you succeed, you are probably playing the movement as a whole too slowly.

25.rh Beethoven's MS here and in the recapitulation (bar 120) appears to distinguish between staccato dots and dashes. Although the marks are not entirely unambiguous and were not observed in **B/C** (which interchange dots and dashes somewhat randomly in this movement), the distinction would certainly make musical sense, with the dots less sharply staccato. See also bars 91–2.

30.rh.1 A six-note trill, starting on the upper note (as was usual at this date), seems best if it can be managed. Small hands can if necessary play the lower note slightly before the trill and not hold it on.

36.rh.2 It seems that Beethoven simply forgot to write in the final turn here (cf. bar 131)

43 The *p* is somewhat ambiguously placed in **A** and could have been intended for the first chord of the bar (cf. bar 137). On the other hand, Beethoven was not averse to creating minor discrepancies of this sort between exposition and recapitulation.

43–56, 137–50 The beaming and stemming have been standardized. In **A** the first chord in the bar is sometimes beamed to the next one (rh.43–7, 140–1, lh.47, 140) and the r.h. chords are sometimes written as two voices (rh.45–8, 138–42), but following no clear pattern and evidently without significance. The staccato marks in bars 43 and 137 are somewhat ambiguous, between dots and dashes, in contrast to the very elongated dashes used for the most part. The implication is that Beethoven was imagining a less emphatic and sharp staccato here than in most other places. Performers should bear this in mind, keeping bars 43–6 and 137–40 relatively light in touch.

47.lh.1 The absence of a staccato may be an oversight, with the assumption that the r.h. staccato also applies to l.h. (where it is added in **B/C**); but it is also absent in the corresponding place in the recapitulation (bar 141) in all sources. The note could therefore be given slight emphasis as the bass of the goal of the preceding phrase and the start of the next.

50–6 Czerny recommends bars 50 and 52 'remarkably ritardando and very staccato', and bars 55–6 'also ritardando and soft, using the pedal for each half of the bar'. You may choose whether to follow this more expressive interpretation or restrict yourself to the plainer version actually written. But either way, the result should be consistent with your overall interpretation of the movement.

59, 61–2 The grace notes should probably be played as rapidly as possible, to match the chords in bars 58 and 60, and because in bar 196 a similar arpeggiated chord has to be contained entirely within the first semiquaver of the bar. On the other hand, some performers may prefer a slower arpeggio, as is implied by Beethoven's use of only two beams for the grace notes, in order to create a more reflective mood.

61–2 As Tovey points out, there should be no crescendo here but, if anything, a slight decrescendo, as was marked in an early sketch for this passage.

79.lh.1, 87.rh.1 Staccato marks are in **B/C** only, but probably authentic (cf. bars 75, 91).

80–2.lh.4–6 Although the swellings are no longer marked, some slight gradation of tone is appropriate.

91–2.rh The distinction between staccato dots and dashes can be made quite effectively here by use of finger staccato and wrist staccato respectively.

100–1 A slight slowing down just before the recapitulation in bar 102 would be in order; but make sure it is only slight, since the long note values do most of the slowing down already.

110.rh.1 The staccato added in **B/C** is probably not authentic (cf. bar 9).

125.rh The slur added here instinctively by Beethoven provides useful evidence that he wanted all similar trills (cf. bars 30, 32, 127) to run into the next chord too.

132 In **A** the *p* is placed one note later; in **B/C** two notes later.

133.lh.2, 4 Staccatos are added in **B/C** but are perhaps not authentic (cf. bar 38). Tovey notes that the compression of bars 38–40 into only two bars here (133–4) is intentional; but interestingly, **A** shows that it is actually bar 39 that is a last-minute interpolation, and the passages originally matched.

143.rh.1 The top note could be an error (cf. bar 49), and certainly gives irregular part-writing, but it is in all the sources. Pianists may wish to make a crescendo in bars 143 and 145, as in bars 49, 51.

163–6 It is possible that Beethoven wanted this passage loud, as some editors have surmised and as might also be deduced from the *p* in bar 167; but there is no such indication in the sources. In **B/C** slurs are added over most of the demisemiquaver groups and the final group of three semiquavers, but they serve little purpose and may not be authentic. Notice that the first two bars are without pedal ('con sordino') but the next two do have pedal. Make the most of this contrast of sonorities.

185–6 It is best to group the notes in fours as shown, rather than making the chromatic scale absolutely smooth. Beethoven often used beaming patterns to suggest slight accentuation, and had he wanted a smooth scale here he would have probably used a single beam like the one in bar 187. The two groups of five in bar 186, however, are beamed as a single group of ten in **A**, perhaps to avoid giving too much prominence to the pitch A. The first note of the final beat is not Cx as before but D♮, which deserves extra emphasis as recalling the Neapolitan sixths of bars 179–80.

187 The trill needs to begin on the main note, and should probably run straight into the cadenza. The quavers should be played smoothly and at approximately their normal speed, but in such flourishes the tempo can be freer than usual. The *p* is missing in **B/C** and is slightly puzzling since it is followed by *decresc.* and then another *p*. It seems best to regard the first *p* more as *mp* (which Beethoven almost never uses) – relatively quiet after the *f* passage but slightly louder than the second *p*.

BARRY COOPER

dedicated to Countess Giulietta Guicciardi

SONATA QUASI UNA FANTASIA
in C sharp minor
('Moonlight')
composed 1801

BEETHOVEN, Op. 27 No. 2
Edited by Barry Cooper

Adagio sostenuto

Si deve suonare tutto questo pezzo delicatissimamente e senza sordino

Attacca subito il seguente

Allegretto

La prima parte solamente una volta

[Fine]

Trio

Allegretto d.c.